I Met a Bully on the Hill

I met a Bully on the Hill

MARTHA BROOKS
AND
MAUREEN HUNTER

I Met A Bully on the Hill
first published 1995 by
Scirocco Drama
An imprint of J. Gordon Shillingford Publishing Inc.
© Copyright Martha Brooks and Maureen Hunter, 1986

Cover design by Terry Gallagher/Doowah Design
Photo of Martha Brooks by Gerry Kopelow
Photo of Maureen Hunter by Randy Gibson
Printed and bound in Canada by Hignell Printing Ltd.

Published with the generous assistance of The Canada Council.

Canadian Cataloguing in Publication Data

Brooks, Martha 1944-
I met a bully on the hill

A play.
ISBN 1-896239-02-1

I. Hunter, Maureen, 1947- II. Title.
PS8553.R663I25 1995 C812'.54 C95-910267-1
PRQ919.3.B76I25 1995

Production Credits

I Met A Bully on the Hill was commissioned and first produced by Prairie Theatre Exchange, Winnipeg, Canada, as part of its 1986-87 school tour, with the following cast:

J. J. ....Martine Friesen
DAVID ....Vern Thiessen
RAYMOND ....Darrell Baran
KARLA ....Maggie Nagle

Directed by Kim McCaw
Sets and costumes designed by Carole Klemm
Props designed by Wayne Reierson
Stage Manager: Rose Passante

I Met a Bully on the Hill was originally commissioned by Prairie Theatre Exchange for its Theatre for Young Audiences program. It was written for presentation to children in Kindergarten through Grade Three, but is suitable for children in Kindergarten through Grade Six.

Playing time: about 45 minutes.

Setting

The Hill, the Schoolyard, the Bridge

In the original production, the set was designed for presentation in-the-round, with students seated on the floor around the playing area. No stage or special lighting was used. The set pieces, consisting of two boxes and a bridge, were placed on the floor of the school gym or hall. A carpet (20' x 20') was used to differentiate the playing area. One of the boxes (1' high x 2'6" wide by 5' long) represented the hill. Another box (1' high by 2'3" wide by 2'3" long) was used for extra seating and, later, as a second base for the bridge. The bridge (2'6" high by 1'6" wide by 3' long) had holes carved into the upper portion, large enough to attach handcuffs to. The boxes and the bridge were made of plywood and painted.

Cast

J. J. (JONQUIL JOSEPHINE) An eight-year-old girl who has just moved in from the country. She is small for her age, sensitive and intelligent but slightly off-centre. She is spunky, has always made friends easily and wears yellow clothing for luck. She has a tendency to babble.

DAVID A small Black eight-year-old boy whose passion is his trumpet. He is intelligent, sardonic and a bit of a know-it-all. He uses his sense of humor to hide a very real sensitivity and to get himself out of tight spots. His idol is Wynton Marsalis, the classical/jazz trumpeter. He wears wire-rimmed glasses.

RAYMOND A husky nine-year-old boy who is repeating Grade Three. He has low self-esteem. He dresses like a "tough." He is bullied by his older sister and is afraid of the dark. He is a pro at terrorizing and demoralizing his victims but displays an undercurrent of humour, and this gives us hope for his future.

KARLA An eight-year-old girl who is large for her age. She is boisterous, tough, warm-hearted and genuine. She is undiplomatic and too hearty.

Martha Brooks

Martha Brooks is the author of *Paradise Café, Two Moons in August* and *Traveling On Into the Light.* Her children's play, *Andrew's Tree,* won the 1991 Chalmer's Award.

Maureen Hunter

Maureen Hunter is the author of six full-length plays includng *Footprints on the Moon, Beautiful Lake Winnipeg, Transit of Venus* (produced by the Royal Shakespeare Company, 1993-94) and *Atlantis*, a work-in-progress.

Scene One

(The hill. A morning in late August. J.J. enters, dressed for school. In her hair is a yellow ribbon. She carries a knapsack with yellow trim and a coffee can with a plastic top, poked full of holes.)

J.J.:   *(To audience.)* Hi. My name's J.J. You might want to ask what that stands for but I'll tell you what. Don't! *(Holds up can.)* See this? There's a caterpillar inside and it's green with black stripes and yellow spots which makes it my favourite kind of caterpillar 'cause it's got yellow on it and yellow's my favourite color. It's my lucky color, too. As long as I wear yellow, nothing bad can happen.

(A shrill trumpet blast is heard, offstage. J.J. frowns, peers in the direction of the sound, shrugs, turns back to the audience.)

My grandpa gave me this caterpillar the day we moved— to keep me company now that I have to live in the city which I don't want to do but I have to anyway. My mum says I'll get used to it and even get to like it someday but I doubt it 'cause even after I got used to Brussels sprouts I didn't like them one bit. *(Sighs.)* But I have to try and like the city now that I live here 'cause I promised my Grandpa I'd try real hard. He's the one who gave me this caterpillar—oh, I already told you that. He said if I took it to school on my first day, everybody would know something about me 'cause nobody knows anything about me now. I'm a stranger.

(DAVID runs on, carrying a trumpet case. He bumps into J.J. and knocks the caterpillar out of her hand.)

J.J.:   Hey!

DAVID: Sorry.

J.J.:   Oh, no!

                (J.J. drops to her knees and searches frantically for the caterpillar.)

                Don't just stand there. Help me.

                (DAVID starts searching. Then a thought strikes.)

DAVID: What are we looking for?

J.J.:   My caterpillar.

DAVID: Does it have a name? Does it come when it's called?

                (DAVID cracks up. J.J. gives him a withering look.)

J.J.:   This is serious, you know.

DAVID: *(Resumes searching.)* Call in the RCMP. "Manhunt begins for small fuzzy—"

J.J.:   It's not fuzzy.

DAVID: "Small not-fuzzy caterpillar." Ah-hah! *(Seizes the caterpillar.)* This is it?! *(Studies it.)* It's not fuzzy.

J.J.:   That's 'cause it's got horns. Either they're fuzzy or they've got horns.

DAVID: Wonder how far it stretches. *(Begins to stretch it.)*

J.J.:   Don't! *(Takes the caterpillar, puts it back in the can.)* I have to take it to school.

DAVID: Why?

J.J.:   For Show and Tell. At my old school last year, we had Show and Tell the very first day and I brought in my beetle collection, but my beetles all got ate up by my pet raccoon, Bandit, who's dead now—not 'cause he ate the beetles—so this year I'm bringing a caterpillar... *(Pauses to breathe.)* I know lots about caterpillars.

DAVID: Really.

J.J.:   Do you want to know why I know lots about caterpillars?

DAVID: Well—

J.J.:   It's 'cause I come from the country. I can name every flower that blooms from May till September. My grandpa taught me. He knows everything there is to know about...everything!

DAVID: Well. Impressive. *(Smiles engagingly.)* I'm David.

J.J.:   I'm J.J.

DAVID: J.J. Neat initials.

J.J.:   You think so?

DAVID: Yeah. Same as J.J. Johnson. *(Pause.)* Trombone. "Stan Getz and J.J. Johnson at the Opera House. *(Sets it up, with sound effects.)* With Oscar Peterson at piano, Ray Brown—bass, Herb Ellis—guitar and Connie Kay—drums." Live recording, 1957. Made jazz history. *(Smiles.)* I know lots about jazz.

J.J.:   *(Pause.)* See the horns? They're green, and shaped like a "V." See, at the front?

DAVID: I like horns. *(With some pride.)* I'm a trumpet man myself.

J.J.:   Yeah, I heard.

DAVID: You did?

J.J.:   Just now.

DAVID: Oh. Well, I'm just starting.

J.J.:   It was good—but loud. Where I come from things are mostly quiet.

DAVID: Right—the country. I was in the country once. I liked the stars.

J.J.:   Stars aren't as bright here. *(Big sigh.)*

DAVID: *(Pause.)* So—you're new. What school?

(RAYMOND enters, unseen by J.J. and DAVID.)

J.J.:   Bennavista.

DAVID: That's Buenavista. *(Hams it up.)* Buenavista! Means beautiful view. You can be bored in all four of the major directions. *(Pause.)* It's my school, too.

J.J.:   Yeah? What grade? 'Cause if you're in the same grade I am, we could probably—

DAVID: Third.

J.J.:   Me, too.

DAVID: C'mon, I'll walk you.

                 (He reaches for the trumpet case but RAYMOND has slipped up behind him and now puts his foot on the case.)

                 Oh, oh.

RAYMOND: Going somewhere?

DAVID: Watch it, Raymond.

RAYMOND: Watch what?

DAVID: Watch your foot.

RAYMOND: Watch your mouth. *(Kicks the case to David.)*

J.J.:   *(To RAYMOND, righteously.)* You shouldn't do that.

RAYMOND: *(Faces her, sneers.)* What's this?

J.J.:   You could wreck it, you know.

RAYMOND: *(Mimics.)* You could wreck it, you know.

J.J.:   Once my grandpa's horse Danny backed up onto my lunch bag which was on the ground where it should not have been and when he shifted away the bag was all squished and there was juice over everything and my three confused flour beetles that I had in a matchbox got drowned. In raspberry juice.

RAYMOND: What planet did she drop from?

J.J.:   My grandpa's name is Gerry and he's the best horse trainer in about three provinces.

DAVID: *(With nervous bravado.)* You two haven't met? Allow me. J.J., this is Raymond. What can I say about Raymond? Raymond is...large. J.J.'s from the country.

RAYMOND: Yeah? What country?

J.J.:   The country country.

RAYMOND: *(Feigns delight.)* Yeah? I bet you like cows.

DAVID: J.J. *(Signals her to clear out.)*

J.J.:   I do. I really like cows.

RAYMOND: *(In her face.)* Mooooo!

DAVID: Come on, J.J.

RAYMOND: Take off, trumpet man.

DAVID: My pleasure. J.J.?

RAYMOND: *(Looms over her.)* Know where you are? Cowgirl?

J.J.:   *(Glances around.)* On a hill.

RAYMOND: On my hill.

J.J.:   Hills don't belong to kids.

RAYMOND: This one does. This one belongs to me. And I don't like cowgirls. From the country. On my hill.

DAVID: *(To J.J.)* What are you trying to do, make the six o'clock news?

J.J.:   Even if it is your hill. You'll just have to share it.

RAYMOND: *(Mimics.)* You'll just have to share it.

J.J.:   You will. I have to use this hill every day to get to school and back. There's no other way. See, that's my house right over there—

DAVID: *(Like an announcer.)* "Grade Three-er wearing yellow ribbon found ground today."

RAYMOND: Say! What you got there?

J.J.:   A caterpillar.

RAYMOND: Let me see.

             (J.J. hesitates.)

             I'm not gonna eat it.

DAVID: Don't count on it.

RAYMOND: *(To DAVID.)* Do you want a knuckle sandwich?

DAVID: *(To J.J.)* Forget it. You'll find out. *(Exits.)*

RAYMOND: Aw, come on. Show me.

             (J.J. draws the caterpillar from the can and hands it to RAYMOND.)

J.J.:   See, he's got little horns.

RAYMOND: He does? Where? *(Feigns interest.)*

J.J.:   Right on top of his little head. Isn't he cute?

RAYMOND: Aw!

J.J.:   When he grows up, he's going to be a beautiful Swallowtail butterfly. I can't wait till he grows up 'cause when he does—

             (RAYMOND drops the caterpillar to the ground and slowly, deliberately, squashes it under his heel. J.J. wails.)

RAYMOND: It's just a stupid bug. *(Leans in.)* Stay off my hill.

             (RAYMOND strides off. J.J., in tears, stares at the remains of her caterpillar.)

J.J.:   What did you have to go and do that for? It didn't do anything to you. It was just a little caterpillar that my grandpa gave me. *(Scrapes up the remains and puts them in the can.)* I knew I wouldn't like it here. I'll never never never never NEVER like it here. *(Exits.)*

Scene Two

(The schoolyard. Morning recess. DAVID and KARLA are trying to get a game of marbles going. RAYMOND stands off to the side, tossing a football. KARLA peers into DAVID's marble bag.)

KARLA: What you got in there? Got a Steely? Ha. A Captain America. I'll play you my Mexican Crock for it.

DAVID: Are you trying to bankrupt me? It's the only one I've got.

KARLA: Take it or leave it.

RAYMOND: Marbles is for babies.

KARLA: *(To DAVID, ignoring RAYMOND.)* Okay. How about a Crystal for your green Pearly?

DAVID: I've got three Crystals and no blue Pearlies.

KARLA: What shade? I've got sky blue and navy blue.

RAYMOND: Marbles is for sissies.

(RAYMOND walks through their game, scattering the marbles.)

KARLA: Take a hike, Raymond.

RAYMOND: Hey, hey, Karla—I'm really scared.

KARLA: It's Killer Karla to you. Remember?

RAYMOND: *(To DAVID.)* Are you gonna play ball, or are you gonna play with girls.

KARLA: He's playing with me.

RAYMOND: No, he's not. He's playing with me.

DAVID: Oh, yeah?

RAYMOND: Yeah. *(Shoves the ball into DAVID's stomach.)*

DAVID: I'm playing with him.

KARLA: All right, then. I'm quarterback.

RAYMOND: I'm quarterback.

DAVID: I'm leaving.

KARLA: *(Grabs his arm.)* No, you're not.

RAYMOND: *(To DAVID.)* You're wide receiver.

KARLA: No, he's fullback.

RAYMOND: He's wide receiver.

KARLA: He's fullback.

DAVID: What ever happened to freedom of choice?

> *(J.J. enters, full of righteous indignation. She strides up to RAYMOND.)*

J.J.:   I've thought about it all morning and I couldn't think of anything else that would be the best thing to do so this is it. *(Kicks his shin.)* That's for killing my caterpillar.

DAVID: She's nuts.

KARLA: *(With admiration.)* She's dead.

> *(RAYMOND, at first taken aback, now turns ominously on J.J. He bunts her backwards with one hand.)*

RAYMOND: You're gonna pay for this. You're gonna wish you'd never been born.

> *(RAYMOND shoves J.J. down. She gets up.)*

J.J.:   Why don't you pick on someone your own size?

> *(RAYMOND shoves her down again.)*

RAYMOND: I'll pick on anyone I want.

J.J.:   *(Fights back tears.)* You big stupid bully!

RAYMOND: *(Points his finger at her.)* I'm not through with you yet. *(Exits.)*

KARLA: Good try, uh…

DAVID: J.J.

KARLA: Jay-Jay. How do you spell that?

J.J.:   You don't spell it. It's J period, J period.

KARLA: So. What does it stand for?

J.J.:   Nothing.

KARLA: Aw, come on. Tell us your name.

J.J.:   I just did.

DAVID: Leave her alone, Karla. If she doesn't want to tell, she
              doesn't want to tell.

KARLA: It must stand for something. Let me see. Jeri Jeritol?
              (Laughs.) Jumping Jehosephats?

DAVID: Jessica Jabber-blabber? *(Cracks up.)*

KARLA: Jeremiah Jampile? *(Howls.)*

DAVID: Just Joking?

              (More laughter. J.J. gives him a dirty look.)

              Just joking.

J.J.:   All right, I'll tell you. You're going to find out anyway.
              Promise not to laugh.

DAVID: Promise.

              *(KARLA and DAVID make ritualistic promise signs.
              Pause.)*

KARLA: Well?

              (Suppressed glee.)

DAVID: We're waiting.

J.J.:   Jonquil Josephine.

(A great commotion. DAVID and KARLA roll on the ground. Groans, vomit jokes, etc.)

You promised! *(Laughs in spite of herself.)* I didn't pick it.

(The school bell rings. DAVID and KARLA gather up their marbles.)

KARLA: Well, I'll say one thing. You've got lots of nerve, standing up to Raymond—a little squirt like you. You've got spunk, kid.

(KARLA gives J.J. a hearty slap on the back, then exits with DAVID.)

J.J.:   Spunk? *(Pause.)* Spunk. Then how come I feel so scared? *(Exits.)*

Scene Three

(The hill. After school that day. RAYMOND enters, flipping through a comic book. Seeing J.J. coming, he hides. J.J. enters, with her knapsack. She starts to move nervously down the hill, like a cat on a hot tin roof. Just when she thinks she's safe, RAYMOND jumps out.)

RAYMOND: Mooooo! *(Moves in on her, beaming broadly.)* Well, look who's here. Little miss cowgirl. With her cute little yellow bow. *(Fingers it.)*

J.J.: Stop it.

(J.J. moves to leave; RAYMOND blocks her.)

Let me past.

RAYMOND: Hey, I'd like to. Honest. But what can I do? You're on my hill.

J.J.: It's not your hill.

RAYMOND: J.J., J.J., J.J. What am I going to do with you? You can't seem to get things through your head. Maybe that's because you're from the country. So I'm going to ask you one more time. *(Leans into her.)* Whose hill is this?

J.J.: Nobody's.

RAYMOND: It's my hill. Isn't it?

J.J.: I guess so.

RAYMOND: I can't hear you.

J.J.: *(Louder.)* It's your hill.

RAYMOND: Very good.

J.J.: I told you, I have to use it.

RAYMOND: You have to use it. Well now, that creates a little problem. See—nobody uses my hill. Hmmmm. *(Thinks about it, then feigns delight.)* I got it! I'll charge you rent.

J.J.:   Rent?

RAYMOND: A quarter.

J.J.:   A quarter!

RAYMOND: A quarter every time I catch you on it.

J.J.:   I can't pay that much. I only get two dollars a week allowance.

RAYMOND: That's your problem, isn't it? *(Extends his hand.)* I'll take the first one now.

J.J.:   I don't have any money right now.

RAYMOND: *(Sighs.)* Tsk, tsk, tsk. *(Sweetly.)* I'll trust you. *(Firmly.)* Next time—bring two quarters. *(Starts to move off, turns back.)* You tell anyone about this, you're dead. *(Exits.)*

J.J.:   A quarter every time he catches me. What am I going to do? I have to use this hill—let's see. To get to school, to get home for lunch, to get back to school after lunch, to get home after school. That's four times a day. Four quarters a day is...*(Counts on her fingers.)* a dollar! Times five days a week—*(Gasp.)*—five dollars a week! I can't do this. How am I going to do this? *(A thought strikes.)* I'll take my lunch to school. Then I'll only have to use the hill twice a day. So that'll be two times five days equals...ten and ten quarters is—two dollars and fifty cents. I can't afford this! And what if my mum won't let me take my lunch to school? *(Resolutely.)* I'll have to think of something. I don't know what, but—something. *(Exits.)*

Scene Four

(The schoolyard. A week later, after school. DAVID enters, with his trumpet, and sits. He appears to be waiting for someone. Bored, he drums his fingers on his trumpet case. Then he opens the lid and reverently takes out his trumpet. He lifts it to his lips, takes a breath, closes his eyes and limbers up his fingers on the keys. He takes another breath. Beat. Sighs. Lowers the trumpet. Lifts the trumpet back to his lips, pretends to play a jazz standard, using his voice as the instrument. The choice of music can be up to the actor. The sound we hear is beautiful, soulful and unexpected—the real DAVID. It reveals his love for music and his longing to be really good. Towards the end of his song, J.J. straggles in, wearing lots of yellow. She stops and listens.)

J.J.: Wow!

(Embarrassed, DAVID fumbles with his trumpet and quickly puts it back in its case.)

I've never heard anything like that. You know what that's like? That's like at night when you stand on the best hill in the country and a million summer stars all fall around you.

DAVID: That's how I want to play my trumpet someday. I don't know if I ever will.

J.J.: You will.

DAVID: Maybe.

J.J.: Of course you will. *(Pause.)* What are you doing here?

DAVID: I was waiting for you.

J.J.: You were?

DAVID: I was. You're famous.

J.J.: Sure.

DAVID: You are. You've got the class record. Four detentions in
                one week. Impressive.

J.J.:   Yeah. Want my autograph?

                *(J.J. sits cross-legged on the ground, throws her
                books down beside her, drops her forehead onto one
                hand.)*

DAVID: What's wrong? What did I say? Are you mad? You're
                crying. Why are you crying? *(Sits next to her, puts an
                arm around her.)* Hey, I was just teasing.

J.J.:   *(Sobs.)* I know.

DAVID: *(Pats her shoulder awkwardly.)* Go ahead and cry, you'll
                feel better. But watch the shirt. No, no, just kidding. You
                go ahead and cry all over it. Get it real wet. You'd be
                doing me a big favour. I hate this shirt. I really hate it. I
                told my mum I wanted a classy striped shirt like Wynton
                Marsalis wears? What does she come home with? *(Pulls
                out the bottom.)* A wimp shirt. Look at it!

J.J.:   I hate this school! I hate everybody here. I want to go
                back to the country. Everything was nice there. I had
                everything I ever wanted in the country. The people I
                knew were nice. They liked me.

DAVID: *(Pats her back vigorously.)* Well, I like you. *(Stands.)*
                Are you feeling better now?

J.J.:   I don't belong here. I don't fit in. When I was in the
                country, I never had to worry about what would happen
                when I went out the door. *(Pause.)* Except when I was six
                and my grandpa had these three White Rock roosters and
                they used to wait for me at the foot of the hill and when I
                came home from school they'd chase me all the way back
                up the hill and bite at the backs of my legs. It was really
                scary and that was just after my dad died which made it
                worse 'cause I felt like I had to act like a big girl so my
                mum wouldn't worry about me, but she did anyway.

DAVID: Gee.

J.J.:   Then one day I came running up the hill with those stupid
                roosters chasing after me and I looked up and there was

my grandpa laughing and laughing. I was so mad at him I started to cry. And then he picked me up and gave me a big hug and he told me if I'd just learn to see what's funny in things I wouldn't be so scared. Easy for him to say. *(Pause.)* I wish my grandpa was here now. He'd know what to do.

DAVID: You mean about Raymond.

J.J.:   Yeah.

DAVID: Know what we call him behind his back?

J.J.:   What?

DAVID: *(Slowly, gleefully.)* Poop-Along.

J.J.:   Poop-Along!

DAVID: Because he is one. He's been the biggest poop around, ever since he failed Grade Three. He's been mean to just about everyone all summer.

J.J.:   I thought it was just me.

              (KARLA enters, kicking a soccer ball.)

KARLA: Hi, guys. *(Executes some fancy manoeuvres.)*

DAVID: *(To J.J.)* No way. Remember the first day of school? When he was jumping all over my trumpet case?

KARLA: Hey, David—catch. *(Throws him the ball.)*

J.J.:   I've never come across anyone like him. I don't know how to handle him.

DAVID: Why don't you ask Karla?

KARLA: Ask me what?

J.J.:   How you handle a bully.

KARLA: Well, I'll tell you how I handle them. *(Matter-of-factly.)* I'm nice to them for a while, and then I beat them senseless.

J.J.:   *(Sighs.)* Must be nice to be big and tough.

DAVID: She used to be a suck.

KARLA: That's right. I let people push me around—call me names. Make me feel like I was just a big ugly worm. Then one day I came home crying to my dad and he said, "You're a big girl, Karla. Next time they bother you, just haul off and punch them a good one in the breadbasket."

J.J.:   And it worked.

KARLA: I only had to do it once or twice. Now they leave me alone. They all leave me alone.

DAVID: That's because you're so meeeean, Karla.

KARLA: *(Struts her stuff.)* Yeah, meeeean. It's like they're afraid I've got something catching. Like leprosy.

DAVID: Or gangrene.

                (With graphic illustrations.)

KARLA: Or beri-beri. Bubonic plague.

DAVID: Elephantiasis.

J.J.:   Hardware disease!

                (Stunned silence.)

                Hardware disease. Animals get that. That's when they start eating all this stuff they're not supposed to eat, like rusty old nails and old pieces of tin and barbed wire. And then it makes them sick. And it's called hardware disease. You can even ask my grandpa.

                (KARLA and DAVID exchange glances.)

DAVID: No kidding? That's really—interesting.

KARLA: Yeah.

J.J.:   *(Pause.)* So if you're not mean, how come they call you Killer Karla?

KARLA: Raymond started that. And before I knew it, everyone was calling me that. I used to like my name.

J.J.:   Not me. I've never liked mine. Jonquil. Josephine.

KARLA: How'd you get a name like that, anyway?

J.J.:   Don't ask. *(Takes a breath, plunges in.)* Well, it's 'cause, Number One, I have an aunt called Josephine who's got these two glass pigs, they're ornaments, that I get to hold when I go to see her, and Number Two, I was born in the spring and my dad's favourite flowers were jonquils. You probably don't know what a jonquil is, it's a member of the daffodil family.

               (Dead silence.)

DAVID: Well. Aren't you glad they didn't call you Daffodil?

KARLA: Then we could call you Daffy, for short.

               (DAVID and KARLA crack up. J.J. takes offense. Pause.)

DAVID: Actually, I don't see what's so wrong with Jonquil Josephine. It's nice. I like it.

J.J.:   It's prissy. I'm not a priss.

KARLA: Right. You just look like one.

               (J.J. turns her back on them.)

               It's not your fault. We can't help the way we look. I mean, you don't look...bad, or anything.

               (DAVID prompts KARLA.)

               I like the yellow, though. Looks good on you. Know what? Yellow's my most favourite color.

J.J.:   Mine, too.

KARLA: I can tell.

J.J.:   I wear it mostly for luck. The more I wear, the luckier I get. Usually. Not lately.

DAVID: *(To KARLA.)* Raymond.

KARLA: So—what's he up to?

J.J.:   *(Seems about to tell, changes her mind.)* Nothing.

DAVID: Right—nothing. Nothing Number One: he calls you
                names. Nothing Number Two: he terrorizes you.
                Nothing Number Three: he makes you sick at your
                stomach so you never want to come to school. Am I
                getting close? Nothing Number Four: he extorts money
                from you.

KARLA: Speak English, David.

DAVID: Extort. It means to hit somebody up for money.

J.J.:   You mean there's a word for what he's doing to me?

DAVID: And others.

J.J.:   Like who?

DAVID: Like me, last summer.

J.J.:   Really? What did you do about it?

DAVID: I told my mother.

J.J.:   That's what I just did!

DAVID: And my mother told his mother, who told his sister.

J.J.:   Oh!

DAVID: End of story.

KARLA: If there's one person Raymond's scared of, it's his sister.

DAVID: And Karla—maybe.

J.J.:   Why's he scared of his sister?

KARLA: She does all kinds of cute stuff. Like locking him in a
                dark closet whenever he's bad.

DAVID: Yeah, one time she left him there for five whole hours.

J.J.:   Five!

KARLA: She wouldn't even let him out to go to the bathroom.

J.J.:   Poor Raymond.

KARLA:	What do you mean, poor Raymond? He's ripping you off, and what I want to know is—how.
J.J.:	The hill. I have to pay rent.
DAVID:	Rent. That's disgusting.
J.J.:	A quarter every time he catches me on it. I don't have that kind of money. I've had to be late for school to miss him. So the teacher's mad at me and gives me all these detentions. And my mum's mad at me 'cause I'm in trouble with the teacher. And last night Mum couldn't sleep 'cause I had nightmares and crawled into bed with her. And this morning she was late for work 'cause we both slept in—it never ends. And it's all because of Raymond.
KARLA:	That jerk! Want me to punch his lights out?
J.J.:	You'd do that for me?
DAVID:	She did it for me, once. I should have sold tickets.
KARLA:	Maybe I could rip one leg off. Or even two. *(Gets into it.)* Maybe I could grab his nose and slowly twist it till it's upside down—
DAVID:	So he'll drown when it rains!
KARLA:	Better yet, why don't we all terrorize him?
DAVID:	Now you're talking.
KARLA:	We could make him crawl through anthills on his hands and knees. Or shove his hand in a jar of slimy things.
DAVID:	Or introduce him to my neighbor's guard dog. Raymond—meet Fang. Fang—meet your breakfast.
KARLA:	It'll be great.
J.J.:	I don't know about this. Anyway, I already told my mum. She's going to call the principal today.
KARLA:	So? Doesn't mean we can't have some fun.
DAVID:	You bet. *(Slaps J.J.'s back.)* We'll fix him.
	(DAVID and KARLA each throw an arm across J.J.'s shoulder. They exit.)

Scene Five

(The next day. Terrorist Mime Sequence with Appropriate Music and Choreography. All characters use a Charlie Chaplin shuffle. Lots of shtick.

RAYMOND enters, Stage Right, with a gym bag. He mimes putting the bag in his locker, slams the door, exits Stage Left. Immediately, J.J., DAVID and KARLA file on, Stage Right, execute a circle, line up in front of the locker. DAVID opens the door. KARLA takes out the gym bag, removes a sandwich from his lunch bag and pours salt in it. DAVID sprays the locker full of Silly String. J.J. hangs back, watching. KARLA puts the bag back in the locker. J.J., DAVID and KARLA flow Stage Left, see RAYMOND coming. The line veers around and out Stage Right. RAYMOND enters, Stage Left, moves to locker, removes gym bag, fumes, storms off, Stage Right.)

Scene Six

*(The hill. After school the same day. J.J., DAVID
and KARLA come tumbling on and occupy the hill.
DAVID carries his trumpet case.)*

DAVID: A pretty nice hill. Wouldn't you say?

KARLA: And it's all ours.

J.J.:   You know? This is the first time I've been on this hill
                   when I haven't been scared out of my mind.

KARLA: We sure showed him, huh?

DAVID::   We sure did. I especially liked the silly string.

KARLA: My personal fave was the salt sandwich.

DAVID: Not bad.

KARLA: Not bad? It was sensational.

J.J.:   Do you think he knows who did it?

KARLA: What if he does?

J.J.:   If he does, I'm mincemeat.

DAVID: He won't ever know.

                   *(RAYMOND enters, behind them. He looms briefly
                   on the crest of the hill, then explodes.)*

RAYMOND: You! Think you're so smart. Stupid little games. You're
                   stupid, all of you, you're just—stupid! Yeah, you're a
                   bunch of losers. Think I don't know who did all that
                   stuff? I know. I know!

KARLA: How'd you get along with the principal, Raymond?

RAYMOND: Fine.

KARLA: I bet.

DAVID: I bet it wasn't too painful.

RAYMOND: You and your dumb trumpet. You carry that thing around like you're somebody special. Without that trumpet you're nothing. You're a big fat zero. You can't even play it. Can you?

KARLA: Shut up, Raymond.

RAYMOND: *(To KARLA.)* You ever heard him play it? He can't.

DAVID: I can so.

RAYMOND: What can you play?

DAVID: I can play.

RAYMOND: What? Name one tune.

DAVID: Never mind.

RAYMOND: Name one.

DAVID: *(Erupts.)* I can play "Silent Night" in the key of C!

RAYMOND: "Silent Night!" *(Sticks his finger down his throat.)*

J.J.:   You don't know anything, Raymond.

KARLA: You can't even pass Grade Three.

RAYMOND: *(Turns on KARLA.)* You! You ugly pig. You could join a freak show, you're so ugly.

KARLA: You're no prize yourself.

RAYMOND: Know what you look like? You look like something that's been run over. And died.

KARLA: Say that again and I'll rip your ears off.

RAYMOND: Yeah, that's all you're good for, Karla. You're good at being tough. Right? Killer Karla. You don't have any real friends.

KARLA: Fat lot you know.

RAYMOND: Who's your friend? Him? Her? These two sucky babies? Get off it. They don't like you.

KARLA: They do so.

RAYMOND: You think they like you? Nobody likes you, Karla.

KARLA: *(Believing it.)* That's not true.

RAYMOND: They pretend to like you because you're big. And tough.

DAVID: That's a lie. I like Karla because—I like her, that's all!

J.J.:   Yeah! Yeah! Raymond—you—you...pick your nose and eat it, too!

RAYMOND: *(To J.J.)* You won't be so brave when I get you alone.

(RAYMOND struts off. Silence. A sense of doom.)

J.J.:   I never should have said that. I'm really in trouble now. He's always going to be waiting for me, up here on his hill.

KARLA: I'm not that tough. If I was that tough, would I have seventeen stuffed animals in bed with me every night? *(Pulls a tiny stuffed animal from her pocket.)* And one in my pocket all the time?

J.J.:   He shouldn't have said that. He shouldn't have said any of those things.

KARLA: I know I'm big—for being eight. But I'll grow into my body someday. That's what my mum says. She says my turn will come.

DAVID: He's right. I can't play my trumpet.

J.J.:   But you will. I know you will.

DAVID: I'll never play like Wynton Marsalis. He started when he was twelve and now he's the best in the world.

J.J.:   So, see? You're only eight. You've got a head start on him.

KARLA: Know what he's done to us? He's made us all feel like we're nothing.

J.J.:   We're not nothing.

DAVID: That's for sure.

J.J.:   We should make a promise right now, never ever to let him do that ever again. Right?

DAVID: Right.

KARLA: Let's take an oath. In blood. *(Pulls a badge from her blouse.)*

DAVID: No way.

KARLA: Come on. You gotta do it.

DAVID: Not in blood. Blood is boring.

J.J.:   I know what. We'll have a secret ceremony. We'll all stand around in a circle, and we'll think of one thing that we own that we really, really like. And then—we'll give it away.

DAVID: I don't get it.

J.J.:   Like, I'll give something of mine to you, and then you'll give something of yours to Karla and then she'll give something of hers to me. And that way we'll each have something that will always remind us that we made this promise. *(Pause.)* And that we're friends. And that we'll stick up for each other.

KARLA: Oh! I get it.

                (J.J. arranges them in a circle, holding hands.)

DAVID: Now what?

J.J.:   Close your eyes and think of whatever it is you like a lot that you could give.

                (They close their eyes. A few beats.)

KARLA: Well…*(Pulls her stuffed animal from her pocket.)* I could give this. I guess.

J.J.:   Do you like it?

KARLA: I really like it.

J.J.:   Okay. I'll give my special yellow ribbon. I never take it off except when I have to wash it. And my mum has to make me. And I wash it real fast so no bad luck can come and get me. But I've got other yellows now. So that's okay.

(KARLA and J.J. turn to DAVID.)

DAVID: I'll give up my shirt.

J.J.:   You hate that shirt.

DAVID: Well...I don't exactly hate it. Very much.

J.J.:   Yeah, but you don't like it. You don't really like it.

DAVID: Well then, what am I going to give?

(J.J. and KARLA turn to look at the trumpet.)

DAVID: Oh no. Not my trumpet. I can't give away my trumpet.

KARLA: You don't have to give it away. But you never even let anybody touch it.

DAVID: *(With great difficulty.)* Okay. Just once. You get to touch it once. While I watch.

          (J.J. slowly removes her ribbon and hands it to KARLA. KARLA takes out her stuffed animal and hands it to J.J. DAVID lifts his trumpet from its case and lays it in KARLA's hands like a living thing.)

J.J.:   Okay. Now we all say, "I promise never to let Raymond make me feel like a nothing again."

ALL: I promise never to let Raymond make me feel like a nothing again.

          (Pause.)

J.J.:   I think things will be better now.

DAVID: I think so, too.

J.J.:   When I first came here I was pretty sure I was never going to like it no matter what, and then I met Raymond and I knew I wouldn't like it, but I'm starting to get the feeling that maybe I might.

(Pause. DAVID looks at his watch.)

DAVID: Holy cow! My trumpet lesson's in five minutes. *(Grabs his trumpet back, picks up his case and runs off.)*

KARLA: J.J.? *(Hesitates.)* Aw, never mind.

J.J.:   What?

KARLA: I guess you wouldn't want to...walk to school with me tomorrow.

J.J.:   Sure!

KARLA: *(Elated.)* Pick you up at quarter to nine.

              (KARLA exits. J.J. starts happily up the hill towards home. Suddenly, RAYMOND appears at the crest of the hill and stands glaring down at her. He has a yo-yo which he manipulates menacingly. J.J. reaches for the empty spot where her yellow ribbon was. Her confidence evaporates.)

RAYMOND: What did I tell you not to do?

J.J.:   What do you mean?

RAYMOND: You know what I mean. I told you not to tell anyone. Didn't I?

J.J.:   I don't remember.

RAYMOND: You don't remember. Want me to jog your memory?

J.J.:   I told my mum.

RAYMOND: Right. And because you told your mum, she told the principal, and now I have a lot of homework to do. Know what? I'm not going to do it. Know who's going to do it? You are. Not just today. Every day. From now on, you're doing all my homework.

              (KARLA enters unseen. RAYMOND holds out his scribbler to J.J. Reluctantly, she reaches for it. He drops it at her feet.)

Nine pages of math. Do it and meet me here right after supper.

(RAYMOND glares at J.J., turns and disappears over the hill. J.J. stares after him. She toys with the scribbler with her foot, picks it up, then angrily throws it down again.)

KARLA: He never learns.

J.J.:   Karla!

KARLA: I don't know why. I just had a feeling I should come back.

J.J.:   Oh, Karla. What am I going to do?

KARLA: Not you. Us. We're going to do plenty. *(Throws her arm across J.J.'s shoulders.)* Now, listen. I'll call David and...

(They exit.)

Scene Seven

(The schoolyard. After supper. KARLA and DAVID run on separately. J.J. straggles on, wearing even more yellow, dragging a blanket. DAVID brandishes a lunch box. At first KARLA seems to be carrying nothing; then she whips out a set of handcuffs.)

DAVID: Handcuffs! Where'd you get them?

KARLA: "Borrowed" them from my dad. *(To J.J.)* He's a cop.

DAVID: Won't he be mad?

KARLA: They'll be back before he knows they're gone.

DAVID: I thought we were going to use rope.

KARLA: What's the difference?

J.J.:   I don't know, Karla. I don't know if we should be doing this.

KARLA: What do you mean? Of course we should.

J.J.:   I'm not so sure. I just talked to my grandpa. I called him long distance and boy was I lucky to even get him 'cause he was almost halfway across the yard on the way to the barn and he practically didn't hear the phone ring but then he did which was lucky for me 'cause I never in my life had a time when I really needed to talk to him when he wasn't there. And anyway he had really good advice.

KARLA: Look, we made a promise.

J.J.:   Sure, but my grandpa says—

KARLA: Never mind your grandpa. We made a promise, remember? And Raymond's making you feel like a nothing—all over again. Isn't he? Well, isn't he?

J.J.:   Well, yeah, but—

KARLA: But what?

J.J.: But this is really mean, Karla. And we don't even need to do it 'cause Grandpa says—

KARLA: Grandpa says!

DAVID: Look, you guys, if we're going to do this, we're going to have to work fast. It's getting late.

KARLA: Come on, let's go.

(KARLA and DAVID run off. J.J. hesitates, then runs after them.)

Scene Eight

(The bridge. Immediately following. DAVID and KARLA run on, with the lunch box and handcuffs. J.J. runs on with the blanket and RAYMOND's scribbler. DAVID and KARLA hide under the bridge. J.J. sits on it, opens the scribbler and pretends to be finishing RAYMOND's homework. RAYMOND enters.)

RAYMOND: Ha! I knew you'd be here. Have you got it done?

J.J.:   Just about.

RAYMOND: Hurry up. I haven't got all night.

J.J.:   There.

(Closes the scribbler, stands.)

RAYMOND: Bring it.

J.J.:   Raymond, maybe you should just go on home.

RAYMOND: Bring it.

J.J.:   I really mean it. You really should just go home.

RAYMOND: I'm telling you to bring it here.

J.J.:   All right, you can have it.

(J.J. drops the scribbler and steps back. RAYMOND shrugs and moves downhill to the bridge.)

RAYMOND: You better have got it right.

(He picks up the scribbler and flips through it. DAVID and KARLA jump out from under the bridge.)

DAVID: Hi-yaaa!

(DAVID leaps on RAYMOND's back. KARLA tosses J.J. the handcuffs. RAYMOND lunges for J.J.)

KARLA: Hey, Raymond!

                 (RAYMOND moves to slug KARLA. She ducks, grabs one arm and pins it behind his back as DAVID slides off.)

                 Come on, J.J.

DAVID: Come on!

                 (J.J. can't move. DAVID grabs the handcuffs and handcuffs RAYMOND's free arm to the bridge.)

RAYMOND: Hey! Let me go!

KARLA: Not tonight, Poop-Along.

                 (With his free hand, RAYMOND takes a swing at KARLA. He misses.)

DAVID: Not all night.

RAYMOND: What do you mean?

KARLA: Figure it out.

RAYMOND: You're not gonna leave me here!

DAVID: You bet we are.

RAYMOND: But it's gonna get dark...

KARLA: Yeah. Real dark.

RAYMOND: You better not do this.

J.J.:   *(Softly.)* We better not do this.

KARLA: This is what you get for being a bully.

DAVID: For calling people names and making fun of them.

KARLA: For making them pay you rent and do your homework.

DAVID: And, most of all, for scaring them when they're too little to scare you back.

RAYMOND: I didn't mean it.

KARLA: Oh, sure.

RAYMOND: *(To J.J.)* I was only going to make you do my homework
              once.

KARLA: I bet.

RAYMOND: Honest! *(To J.J.)* I just wanted to teach you a lesson.

DAVID: You're the one who needs to be taught a lesson.

RAYMOND: Listen. Just let me go and I tell you what. I'll never pick
              on any of you again. I promise.

KARLA: You promise!

RAYMOND: I do!

KARLA: How dumb do you think we are?

DAVID: Raymond, it's time you learned how it feels to be pushed
              around. And put down.

RAYMOND: Aw, that's just kidding around. You play that trumpet—
              pretty good.

DAVID: Pretty good?

RAYMOND: You play it—really good, David.

DAVID: You're getting warm.

KARLA: What about me, Raymond? Haven't you got anything to
              say to me?

RAYMOND: Sure. What?

KARLA: Like, you know—how I'm the prettiest, most popular
              girl in school.

RAYMOND: Well...you could be. What do I know?

KARLA: Not much. *(To DAVID.)* Let's go.

DAVID: *(Starts off.)* Good night, sleep tight.

KARLA: Don't let the—rats bite. *(Hoots.)*

                    (DAVID and KARLA run off.)

RAYMOND: No. Don't leave me here. Please!

KARLA: *(Off.)* J.J.! Come on.

              (J.J. doesn't move. Throughout this scene, she has been immobilized by the horror of what's happening.)

RAYMOND: J.J.?

J.J.:   We'll let you go in the morning. Promise.

RAYMOND: Don't go. Okay? *(Fights tears.)* I'm scared.

J.J.:   *(Starts to back off.)* I'm sorry.

RAYMOND: I mean I'm really scared...of the dark. J.J.?

DAVID: *(Off.)* J.J.!

              (J.J., distressed, torn, hesitates.)

J.J.:   It'll be all right. Don't be scared, okay? *(Pulls a yellow plastic monster from her pocket, hands it to him.)* Here, hold this. It's yellow. Just hold it tight.

              (RAYMOND looks at the monster and lets it drop. J.J. backs away, exits.)

RAYMOND: Don't leave me here! *(Tests the handcuffs, glances around.)* It's getting dark.

              (He reaches for the blanket, pulls it to his chest, then slowly sinks to the ground. He sees the yellow monster, hesitates, picks it up. Then he looks around fearfully, curls into the fetal position, pulls the blanket over his head and huddles against the ground.)

Scene Nine

(The schoolyard. Immediately following. DAVID and KARLA run on and flop down.)

DAVID: That was the right thing to do.

KARLA: You bet.

DAVID: The only way Raymond's ever going to stop picking on people is to get a taste of his own medicine.

KARLA: That's right.

DAVID: If I'd been as mean to him as he's been to me, I'd be dead meat.

KARLA: He won't be so sure of himself in the morning.

DAVID: Sometimes, you have to be really hard on people to make them understand. Like when I broke my dad's gold watch, I had to pay a dollar out of my allowance every week for ten weeks—to help get it fixed.

KARLA: And when I was supposed to be watching my little sister and she got into the cough medicine and drank it, and got really sick, I was grounded for a month. I deserved it, too.

(J.J. drags on, sits next to them.)

DAVID: You have to accept responsibility for your actions. That's what my dad says.

KARLA: Raymond has made lots of people unhappy.

DAVID: Now he's unhappy. That's fair.

(Silence.)

J.J.:   Does his sister really lock him in a dark closet?

DAVID: All the time.

J.J.:   No wonder he's afraid of the dark. Once I got locked in Grandpa's cellar. It was only for ten minutes, but I just about went crazy.

KARLA:	He's not in a closet. Or a cellar. He's outside. In the fresh air. With all the stars.
DAVID:	And he won't get cold—we gave him a blanket. He won't get hungry—we left him some food. Right?
KARLA:	Right.
J.J.:	But he's just a little kid.
KARLA:	He's a bully.
J.J.:	Yeah, but now I feel like a bully. And I don't like that.

(Another silence.)

We can't do this. You know why? It makes us just as bad as Raymond.

KARLA:	He started it.
J.J.:	Two wrongs don't make a right. That's what my grandpa says.
KARLA:	You know what, J.J.? I'm sick and tired of hearing about your stupid grandpa.
J.J.:	He is not stupid. He's the smartest man I ever met. He's a lot smarter than you, Karla—or me, or David. He knows about things. He knows.
DAVID:	Okay, J.J., tell us what he knows.
KARLA:	Since you're going to anyway.
J.J.:	When I called him today? He said to try and think of Raymond as someone who really needs help. And he said, "J.J., you're not the one to help him. You're too little. He needs a big person. So you've got to tell somebody."
KARLA:	Yeah, right. You already told your mum, and look what happened.
J.J.:	Well, maybe I have to keep telling her. And maybe I have to tell the teacher, and the principal. Maybe I just have to keep telling and telling until people finally start listening

to me. And Raymond gets help. And we stop getting bullied.

DAVID: They're going to call you a tattle-tale.

J.J.:   So? It's better than feeling the way I feel now. *(Stands.)* I'm going back. I'm going to let him go. *(Pause.)* Are you guys coming?

KARLA: Nope. I'm staying right here.

DAVID: I think I'm going with her.

KARLA: You think?

DAVID: I am going with her. *(Stands.)*

KARLA: He's not going to stop, you know. He's going to go right on being a big fat jerk.

J.J.:   I don't believe that.

KARLA: What if you're wrong?

J.J.:   *(Pause.)* We'll have each other. Won't we?

DAVID: Yeah.

            (Silence.)

KARLA: Let's go back.

            (KARLA stands. They all run off.)

Scene Ten

(The bridge. A few minutes later. RAYMOND lies huddled against the ground, crying and shivering. J.J., DAVID and KARLA enter cautiously. RAYMOND is at first unaware of their presence.)

RAYMOND: It's gonna be all right. Somebody will come. Somebody's got to come.

J.J.: Raymond?

(RAYMOND wipes his eyes with the back of one hand. He quickly turns, leaps to his feet.)

RAYMOND: Get away from me. Jerks.

(KARLA moves to unlock the handcuffs. RAYMOND shoves her away.)

What are you doing? What are you trying to do to me?

KARLA: We're trying to let you go, Raymond.

RAYMOND: About time.

(KARLA unlocks the handcuffs. RAYMOND moves quickly away, pulling the blanket around him.)

J.J.: Are you all right?

RAYMOND: No, I'm not all right. I'm cold. Don't you know it's cold out here?

J.J.: You were scared.

RAYMOND: Was not. Wasn't scared one bit.

KARLA: How come you're crying?

RAYMOND: Get lost.

J.J.: We're sorry we did this, Raymond.

RAYMOND: Leave me alone.

DAVID: We are. Really.

J.J.:   It was an awful thing to do.

RAYMOND: *(Pause.)* I'da never done that to you. Think you can do something like that to me, and I'll stop? Nobody tells me what to do.

KARLA: Oh, don't be so tough. Everybody gets told what to do by somebody, sometime.

RAYMOND: The whole time, I just kept telling myself, "Somebody's going to come." Only I hoped that somebody wouldn't be my sister.

J.J.:   She's mean, isn't she?

RAYMOND: She's really mean.

DAVID: *(Under his breath.)* She's so mean, I'll bet she eats stucco for breakfast.

KARLA: Yeah. She's so mean—

DAVID: She pours motor oil on her salad.

J.J.:   And eats it with a pitchfork!

RAYMOND: *(Very serious.)* She's so mean she eats pitchforks.

              (They all laugh. Pause.)

J.J.:   Hey, you didn't eat anything.

DAVID: Yeah, you better eat something, Raymond. *(Offers him the lunch box.)*

KARLA: Get your strength back.

RAYMOND: I'm not that dumb. You did something to it.

DAVID: No, honest. It's perfectly fine. Go on. Have a sandwich.

RAYMOND: *(Tempted.)* What kind?

DAVID: Peanut butter, ham, lettuce, tomato—and mayonnaise. Made it myself.

(RAYMOND remembers the monster in his hand. He looks at it, glances at J.J., and stuffs the monster in his pocket. Then he takes a sandwich and bites into it.)

RAYMOND: Not bad.

(The others watch him hungrily.)

DAVID: There's more. There's a side order of my mum's red hot homemade dill pickles.

(RAYMOND takes all the food out of the bag.)

RAYMOND: Good. Thanks.

(RAYMOND starts to move off. The others stare after him. Long faces.)

KARLA: You're not going to eat everything.

RAYMOND: *(With his mouth full.)* Sure, why not?

J.J.:   All by yourself?

RAYMOND: I'm hungry. You'd be hungry, too, if you'd been tied to a bridge. By a bunch of little jerks.

(RAYMOND exits. Stunned silence.)

DAVID: Jeez...

KARLA: What a prince.

J.J.:   He did say thanks.

KARLA: Big deal.

J.J.:   *(Long pause.)* You know, this is just like the time that old stray cat came to live in my grandpa's barn. That cat was the lonesomest, angriest cat. It was ugly, too. Grandpa said he couldn't get near it, and that somebody must have kicked it around lots, and that's why it came to live in his barn. He used to feed it milk fresh from the cow. And he left chops out for it, and even left a blanket out in the winter. He was just so nice to that cat, and that cat was never nice to him. But Grandpa said, "Someday that cat will appreciate what I've done for it."

DAVID: And it did.

J.J.:   Nope. It never did.

              (Pause.)

DAVID: You know, J.J. You're pretty weird…but you have a way
              of making sense. Sort of.

KARLA: *(Slaps J.J. on the back.)* Yeah, you're okay, kid.

J.J.:   *(Big smile.)* Come on. I'll race you guys to the top of the
              hill.

              (They all run off. End of play.)